BRITAIN'S 🏰 HERITAGE

Stationary Steam Engines

Anthony Coulls

AMBERLEY

Acknowledgements

I would like to thank my father Peter Coulls for proof reading the text. Colin Harris provided the photos of colliery winding engines, Andrew Hurrell the photo of the Newcomen engine on page 7 and Alain Foote took the photo of the Willans Central Valve engine on page 53. Other images are by the author or Peter Coulls or are from the Peter Coulls collection.

This book is dedicated to Mike Jacques, who gave me my first lessons in running a beam engine at Snibston, John Davidson and Howard Sharples at the Science & Industry Museum in Manchester, who taught me to run the many engines there, my colleagues at the London Museum of Water & Steam and the many friends I have made across the country who keep this aspect of steam heritage alive for all to enjoy.

First published 2019

Amberley Publishing
The Hill, Stroud
Gloucestershire, GL5 4EP

www.amberley-books.com

Copyright © Anthony Coulls, 2019

The right of Anthony Coulls to be identified as the Author of this work has been asserted in accordance with the Copyrights, Designs and Patents Act 1988.

ISBN 978 1 4456 9107 7 (paperback)
ISBN 978 1 4456 9108 4 (ebook)

British Library Cataloguing in Publication Data.
A catalogue record for this book is available from the British Library.

Printed in the UK.

Contents

1
Introduction: Origins, Down the Mine, Principles and Pioneers

The quiet powerhouses of the industrial revolution, stationary steam engines provided the driving force behind every manufacturing process for well over a century, as well as providing drainage of mines and allowing clean water supplies for the majority of our larger towns and cities. From a small sewage pump at the edge of a field of a few horsepower to a 12,000 horsepower leviathan rolling armoured plate for battleships, these gentle giants of the steam age kept working quietly for decades, unseen by many but often loved and cared for by the men who operated and maintained them. The engine houses they were kept in could be plain or ornate, and a variety of boilers provided the steam for them. This book looks at all these aspects and what it was like to run a large steam engine for industry. The legacy of these iron

There are steam engines preserved to visit all over the country. In London is perhaps the mecca, the London Museum of Water & Steam at Kew Bridge. This view of the Steam Hall shows a handful of the wide selection of engines on view.

Some engines are kept in museums but a large number still survive on their original site, such as this 70-inch cylinder Cornish pumping engine by Harveys of Hayle in Cornwall. Many miles from home, it was erected at Prestongrange in East Lothian in 1874 and is open for visiting.

giants is seen in the dozens of engines preserved for posterity all over the UK, in museums or in their original locations, giving thousands of people the chance to see them and enjoy getting involved in their care and display.

First and foremost, what is steam? Steam is water in the form of a gas, and it is invisible. What is commonly called 'steam' is the visible water vapour which results as the gas condenses back into a liquid. Steam is produced when water is heated to the boiling point of 100 degrees Centigrade, and if confined within a restricted space, it begins to produce a force greater than atmospheric pressure. That force can then be used to bear upon a surface and create motion. In its basic form that is the steam engine, and the most basic engine known was Hero of Alexandria's Aeolipile of around 50 AD, where the steam was used to create rotary motion when released from a sphere of water mounted on an axis – a primitive steam turbine, but essentially a steam toy.

A steam engine is a heat engine that performs mechanical work using steam as its working fluid. In simple terms, the steam engine uses the expansion principle of chemistry, where heat applied to water evaporates the water into steam, and the force generated pushes a piston back and forth inside a cylinder. This pushing force is typically transformed, by way of a connecting rod and flywheel, into rotational force for work. The term 'steam engine' is generally applied only to reciprocating engines as just described, not to the steam turbine. After use in the engine, the reduced-pressure steam is then exhausted to the atmosphere or condensed and pumped back into the boiler.

Left: Simple but effective, Hero's Aeolipile has provided entertainment for centuries. A basic demonstration of steam power, every other engine is a refinement of these principles of fire, water and pressure.

Below: The basic parts and essential working of the stationary steam engine are summed up by this splendid diagram at Middleport Pottery in Stoke-on-Trent.

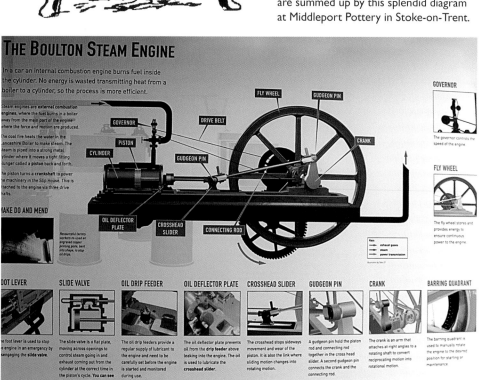

THE BOULTON STEAM ENGINE

In a car an internal combustion engine burns fuel inside the cylinder. No energy is wasted transmitting heat from a boiler to a cylinder, so the process is more efficient.

Steam engines are external combustion engines, where the fuel burns in a boiler away from the main part of the engine where the force and motion are produced.

The coal fire heats the water in the Lancashire Boiler to make steam. The steam is piped into a strong metal cylinder where it moves a tight fitting plunger called a **piston** back and forth.

The piston turns a **crankshaft** to power the machinery in the Slip House. This is attached to the engine via three drive shafts.

GOVERNOR

The governor controls the speed of the engine.

FLY WHEEL

The fly wheel stores and provides energy to ensure continuous power to the engine.

Labels on diagram: FLY WHEEL · GUDGEON PIN · DRIVE BELT · GOVERNOR · PISTON · CYLINDER · GUDGEON PIN · CRANK · OIL DEFLECTOR PLATE · CROSSHEAD SLIDER · CONNECTING ROD

Key:
→ exhaust gases
→ steam
→ power transmission

MAKE DO AND MEND

Resourceful factory workers re-used an engraved copper printing plate, bent into shape, to stop oil drips.

FOOT LEVER	SLIDE VALVE	OIL DRIP FEEDER	OIL DEFLECTOR PLATE	CROSSHEAD SLIDER	GUDGEON PIN	CRANK	BARRING QUADRANT
The foot lever is used to stop the engine in an emergency by disengaging the **slide valve**.	The slide valve is a flat plate, moving across openings to control steam going in and exhaust coming out from the cylinder at the correct time in the piston's cycle. **You can see this working in the model behind you.**	The oil drip feeders provide a regular supply of lubricant to the engine and need to be carefully set before the engine is started and monitored during use.	The oil deflector plate prevents oil from the **drip feeder** above leaking into the engine. The oil is used to lubricate the **crosshead slider**.	The crosshead stops sideways movement and wear of the piston. It is also the link where sliding motion changes into rotating motion.	A gudgeon pin hold the piston rod and connecting rod together in the cross head slider. A second gudgeon pin connects the crank and the connecting rod.	The crank is an arm that attaches at right angles to a rotating shaft to convert reciprocating motion into rotational motion.	The barring quadrant is used to manually rotate the engine to the desired position for starting or maintenance.

6

No one person 'invented' the steam engine. So often it is suggested that James Watt saw a kettle boiling and took inspiration from that, but the truth is rather more prosaic. A number of people over decades developed an engine operated by steam power, each one making alterations and innovations to arrive at the stationary steam engine as recognised over the last 200 years. Many are well known, even more innovators less so, and this book cannot do justice to them all. However, the names of Denis Papin, Thomas Savery and Thomas Newcomen paved the way for the work of James Watt and Richard Trevithick, and each will have a few words here to set their achievements in context in the story of the steam engine. The first real date to make a mark on the history book after Hero is 1690, when Denis Papin created an engine which used the power of steam to raise a piston. He was followed in 1698 when the 'machine for raising water by use of fire' was created by Savery – it had no working parts and in essence used the vacuum created by condensing steam to draw water from a mine. Thomas Newcomen from Dartmouth took the principle of using atmospheric pressure pressing down on a piston, under which there existed a vacuum, to drive a mechanical pump to pump water. The principle was tried out in the Earl of Dudley's collieries in 1712 with great success, though the machine was greatly inefficient due to the heating and cooling of the cylinder that needed to take place – but it worked! It was expensive to make as the precise barrel of the cylinder needed to be bored smooth and thus brass was the best option. A breakthrough would come later in the eighteenth century with the casting of iron cylinders by John 'Iron Mad' Wilkinson of Bersham in North Wales and the cost of the engines went down, making their use much more widespread.

A fully operational replica Newcomen engine was built in the 1980s at the Black Country Living Museum and is run on the same cycle as the original from 1712, made for the Earl of Dudley. It's well worth seeing to observe how steam power began in a commercially successful way.

The creation of a viable and affordable pumping engine staved off an energy crisis, as the Newcomen engine was able to pump flood water out of mines, allowing coal to be gained from greater depths than previously possible. The large coal reserves of the country could be exploited and used as fuel for the industrial growth that was taking place at the time. Within a century of Newcomen's first engine for the Earl of Dudley, 80 per cent of the world's coal was being mined in Britain.

Did you know?

The place of Thomas Newcomen in engineering history was recognised in the early twentieth century by the creation of the Newcomen Society. The only learned society devoted to the study of the history of engineering and technology, it still thrives today and bears tribute to the name of the famous Devonian pioneer. The steam engine still figures prominently in members' research and writings.

By 1775 there were more than 100 atmospheric engines at work in the North East of England alone. While effective, the Newcomen engine was tremendously inefficient, but coal was cheap and plentiful. However, a major problem in the operation was the continuous heating

The 1820 Boulton & Watt engine at Kew Bridge was converted to the Cornish cycle in the 1840s and is one of the few beam engines that one can stand back and appreciate in its entirety while in its own engine house.

and cooling of the cylinder to allow atmospheric pressure to do its work as the steam in the cylinder was condensed to create a vacuum on every stroke. James Watt came upon the idea of a separate condenser and a double-acting cylinder – where steam is applied to either side of the piston in turn. This meant that each end of the cylinder was sealed rather than one end being left open for the atmospheric pressure to push the piston down. Power and efficiency began to rise – fuel consumption was cut by up to 75 per cent in some cases – and the two variables were major players in the development of the stationary steam engine over the next couple of centuries. Watt made the steam engine a universal power source, which could drive any type of machinery, anywhere. The steam engine could run all day long without rest and only needed coal and water – so factories no longer needed to be sited next to rivers, and the growth of industrial towns was a further effect of this innovation.

In 1769, James Watt took out a patent that allowed him to dominate steam engine design and innovation. This in effect prevented other engineers from serious alternative development of the steam engine. The expiry of that patent in 1800 paved the way for a new generation of engineers and experimenters, including Richard Trevithick, who we shall meet again shortly.

While all large beam engines were house-built – meaning that the building they were in formed part of the supporting structure – to a greater or lesser extent, it does make understanding a beam engine difficult when you can't see the whole machine. The exceptions to the rule are only due to preservation, with the Greensplat engine now shown at the Poldark Mine, Wendron Forge, displayed externally with no engine house. Its workings are laid bare, with only a structural wall to support the beam. Occasionally operated by hydraulic power, it shows the full principle unfettered by walls. Similarly, there is an 1817 Grazebrook Foundry blowing engine on outdoor display at Dartmouth Circus in Birmingham.

At Wheal Kitty, near St Agnes in Cornwall, the mine pumping engine house burned down in 1905, exposing the engine itself and the supporting wall for the beam. The loss of an engine was disastrous for a mine, which was reliant on it for draining water from underground.

Poldark Mine at Wendron Forge, Helston, exhibits a Cornish pumping engine completely in the open. Dating from around 1850, it came to the museum from Greensplat Clayworks.

Did you know?

The steam pumping engine found very many applications across the United Kingdom. Even the Spa Pump Rooms in the town of Leamington Spa had a Watt beam engine of a few horsepower installed in the early 1800s!

Despite the innovations, the pressure that the Watt and Newcomen engines ran on was fairly low – between 4 and 12 pounds per square inch on average, reflecting the amount of power in an engine that ran on atmospheric pressure. In early publications about Newcomen engines and their operation, leaks in the haystack pattern boilers were recommended to be 'plugged with a turf'! They were called haystacks on account of the shape of the vessel itself. To get a greater power output, engines were made larger and larger, and of course had to be built into an engine house that supported the engine itself. It was another Cornishman, Richard Trevithick, who set the path for the next stage of the steam engine, which allowed the miniaturisation of the technology and arguably set its path for even greater world domination. Trevithick experimented with higher pressure in his boilers and engines, calling it 'strong steam'. He went to Coalbrookdale in Shropshire in 1802, where the Coalbrookdale Company made the first commercial high-pressure boilers and later the first steam railway locomotive.

The use of higher pressure also increased the risk of boiler explosions, leading James Watt to protest strongly, suggesting that Trevithick 'deserved to be hung'. Trevithick responded by going somewhere where his experience and ability were welcomed and encouraged: South Wales. He made smaller high-pressure engines for transport purposes and stationary power applications. There was a similarity between the designs, and one of his stationary engines was put into a boat. Later on, some of the Trevithick engines built by the Hazeldine Company at Bridgnorth in Shropshire bore very striking similarities to the 1808 locomotive *Catch Me Who Can*, built to run on a circular track in London. The technology went international as a woodcut shows a model being taken ashore in South America; however, the engineer himself, while an innovator, was no businessman and he died penniless in Dartford. The concept of the high-pressure steam engine had been proven nonetheless and small, compact, less expensive but powerful engines took their place in industrial development alongside the massive beam and vertical engines already installed and accepted as power sources. The Cornish cycle beam engine ran at a higher pressure than the Watt machine and set the standard for greater efficiency than that simply offered by the separate condenser and double-acting cylinder where the steam drove the piston in both directions.

Illustrating the compactness possible with a high-pressure engine, the Hazeldine company stationary engine at the Science Museum is of a basic Trevithick design that could be adapted for stationary, maritime or locomotive use.

2
Going Round in Circles

The beam engine was good for pumping and blowing, whether it was water or air, but there was soon the realisation that the Watt engine had a power that could be harnessed for other things. Instead of an engine pumping water to form a head to run a water mill, how about using the engine to drive the mill itself? This would free the mill owners from locating their businesses along watercourses and allow wider development as long as coal and water could be supplied. The challenge of finding a way to turn the up and down motion into a rotary motion was one to be met. The man who finally did it was James Pickard, who patented the crank in 1780. This was to become the normal method for most conventional steam engines for the next two centuries. To get round the patent, James Watt patented the sun and planet gear invented by William Murdoch, whereby a fixed gear on the end of the connecting rod went around another gear on the drive shaft and created rotary motion. Patented in October 1781, one of the earliest Watt engines to have sun and planet gear survives in the collection of the Science Museum in London, where it is displayed as the 'Lap Engine' due to the lapping machines it drove in its working life. As with the early pumping engines, there is a great deal of timber in its construction, which as engine technology progressed, was replaced by iron and steel. It has been said that the profession of engineer arose from millwrights and looking at the very old engines, one can see the direct link between the two.

Development of the steam engine was swift after the 1780s; true, there was the matter of the various patents that Watt had taken out, but engines were made in their dozens across the country as the Industrial Revolution took its course. Matthew Boulton, James Watt's business partner, is recorded as saying 'I sell what everyone desires ... power', and this was very true. There was a demand for more powerful engines, but size was

Dating from 1788, this Watt rotative engine still bears the 'sun and planet' gear to create rotary motion. Known as the 'Lap Engine', it was used in Boulton & Watt's own works.

Despite the widespread adoption of Watt's principles, the atmospheric engine did not die completely. In 1791, the engine illustrated here was made for a Derbyshire colliery. Bearing a cast iron beam, it worked until 1918, quite some feat.

a major constraint, so other solutions were sought. The layout of engines was experimented with, as was fitting a second cylinder to a beam engine to add power. A follow-on from this was the realisation that exhaust steam still had pressure which would allow a second cylinder to do useful work at that lower pressure. This was the concept of the compound engine, where the steam was used twice. As the nineteenth century moved on, sometimes the steam was used three times in three steam cylinders and the triple-expansion engine was created. Despite these innovations, many older engines continued in use for decades – the Newcomen engine preserved in the Science Museum in London worked from 1791 to 1918.

The use of higher-pressure steam as pioneered by Trevithick allowed the engines to be made smaller; this also reduced the need for them to be built into the engine house as most of the beam engines since Newcomen had needed to be. Beam engines for pumping continued to be built into the early twentieth century, but by then free-standing engines mounted in engine rooms and workshops had become commonplace. Experimenting with directly connecting the cylinder to the crank without a beam was also a space saver, and the vertical engine as seen in the North East resulted. In the early days of development, horizontal engines were not progressed as it was felt that having the cylinder on its side would lead to uneven wear.

The last beam engines built for home use in the United Kingdom were constructed in the early years of the twentieth century. Survivors of those late engines include the two

Above: The final flowering of the beam engine was in the early years of the twentieth century. 1900 saw the construction of two Woolf compound-type engines for Coleham in Shrewsbury by Renshaws of Stoke-on-Trent.

Left: In 1904, Holmans of Cornwall sent a beam engine to the Dorothea slate quarry in North Wales. Still standing over a century later, it awaits a secure future despite heritage protection.

The Tees Cottage engine at Darlington remains in full working order and is open to the public about half a dozen times a year. It is conserved rather than restored and gives a good impression of an engine in its original environment.

made for pumping at Coleham in Shrewsbury, now a museum. Standing out and alone is the Dorothea engine at the slate quarry of that name in the Nantlle Valley of Snowdonia – the engine is a Scheduled Ancient Monument, but even now defies any attempts at preservation or restoration. The final late beam engine is the single one at Tees Cottage Pumping Station in Darlington, built locally in 1905 and now run by a society alongside the gas engine that replaced it in 1915 and the later electric pumps that displaced that in turn.

Did you know?

In the UK, there are only two locations able to show the transition from steam through internal combustion to electric on one site. These are Tees Cottage in Darlington and the Kew Bridge site of London's Museum of Water & Steam, both museums of water supply.

It wasn't just for winding men and coal or pumping water and sewage that the rotative engine found use. Anything that involved rotary motion could employ one – and a major use was that of sawmills. Combe Mill at Blenheim is one survivor. Likewise, other kinds of mill – bone and flint mills plus potteries for clay. The steam engine became a driving force behind industrialisation. Steam winches and hoists, small pumps and cranes: so many jobs and steam engines did most of them. Other existing steam engines operating industrial plants include Middleport Pottery in Staffordshire and Bursledon Brickworks in Hampshire. Both these sites are rarities in the twenty-first century and venerated as such, but are representative of thousands of locations and applications during the industrial period.

A major use of the stationary steam engine was the generation of electricity – a whole new industry grew up around the innovative power that would still rely in many cases on steam for its production until the twenty-first century. The large reciprocating engine

Left: Middleport Pottery in Stoke-on-Trent displays this simple single-cylinder engine, typical of thousands of industrial applications of steam power. Built in 1888 by Boulton of Burslem, engines like it could be found nationwide.
Below: The steam-powered production of electricity came in all shapes and sizes. This small engine was made by Dugdill of Stockport and lit a shop window in Bolton as a novelty. Today it can be seen at the Science & Industry Museum in Manchester.

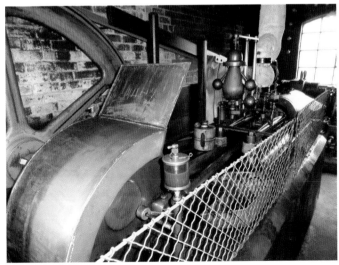

Above: Also at the Science & Industry Museum is this S. Z. de Ferranti cross-compound engine, which provided electric power for around twenty years, after which it was superseded by turbines and sold for use as a mill engine. The generator acts as a flywheel in this application from 1900.

Right: Still in the location it has always occupied, this single-cylinder horizontal engine generates electricity at Clay Mills Pumping Station near Burton upon Trent.

found itself built into power stations driving generators for direct current by ropes, and small engines for commercial and domestic situations reflected the other end of the spectrum. A single-cylindered engine of this type can be seen with a small open-frame dynamo in the Power Hall at the Science & Industry Museum in Manchester, not far from a large twin-cylindered engine by Ferranti for making power for industrial enterprise.

At Clay Mills Pumping Station in Staffordshire, a medium-size single-cylindered engine remains in situ with dynamo and switchgear, a superb example of preserving not just the engine but the associated equipment and control system. When it is run, one gets a real impression of an engine doing a job – under load and no simulation necessary. Of course, the equivalent of a portable generator is the showman's steam traction engine – beyond the scope of this book, but in essence the same thing on wheels and able to move itself around.

The main limitation on electricity production by steam is the speed of the turning of the generator/dynamo/alternator and that will be returned to later in this book.

Did you know?

The steam engine was a very saleable commodity. In the nineteenth century, when an engine was taken out of use, it was very rarely broken up for scrap. Instead, it would be advertised for sale and quite often transported many miles to a new owner and perhaps a new use. At the Science & Industry Museum in Manchester, there is a reversing beam engine which is said to have begun life hauling trains on the Liverpool & Manchester Railway. By 1850, it had been moved and was driving a sawmill on the Haydock collieries complex.

Stationary engine development was paralleled with other steam technology, on roads, rails and ships – and as time went by, aspects of stationary power outstripped the other modes as the demand for power and efficiency grew. In many ways, marine steam was the only application which kept pace as, in line with factories, the engine room of a ship is a confined space and the need for maximum power and efficiency is the same. Some steam innovations that worked on stationary mill engines were tried out on railway locomotives, but they were either too complex to be

The Haydock engine is unusual in that it is a beam engine with the facility to reverse the direction the flywheel turns. This has given rise to the surmise that it was once a winding engine for hauling trains on the Liverpool & Manchester Railway.

maintained in a moving context or susceptible to poor track conditions. Likewise, the steam traction engine hardly evolved after the 1870s when the basic outline and layout had been arrived at. The stationary industrial steam engine, however, continued to be developed to a very high specification into the 1920s and engines of 12,000 horsepower were not unknown, with air-operated valve gear which allowed incredibly quick reversing of rolling mill engines in steelworks.

As the railways of the early nineteenth century began to develop, the reversible stationary steam engine became adapted for rail haulage – initially in the absence of mobile locomotives but latterly due to the belief that steam locomotives couldn't pull trains up gradients. Therefore, the first 5 miles of the Stockton & Darlington Railway in County Durham was worked by stationary haulage engines pulling trains over two escarpments before the locomotives took on the trains from Shildon along the more level route. Similarly, four years later, the Liverpool & Manchester Railway was built with winding engines for the last section of the line at Edge Hill in Liverpool; also, the Canterbury &

In County Durham, the side-lever winding engine was almost standard for colliery applications, so when the railways needed steam winders for their inclines, it was the natural choice. This is the Weatherhill winding engine, now demonstrated by electric power daily at the National Railway Museum, York.

Horizontal engines began to be introduced in the 1820s when slide bars were introduced to support the piston rod and prevent uneven wear on engines of this type. An early survivor is the Swannington Engine from the Leicester & Swannington Railway. It ran for over 100 years and, like the Weatherhill engine, is now an exhibit at the National Railway Museum.

Whitstable line in Kent. The famous Rainhill Trials of 1829 were to prove the capability of the steam locomotive and steam winding engines fell out of favour on main lines, though in industrial use there were steam-worked inclines in operation until the 1960s. The Cromford & High Peak Railway in Derbyshire was amazingly still in use until 1963, with a pair of 1829 beam engines which are now preserved in situ. While no engines survive from the Stockton & Darlington, the remains of one of the Canterbury & Whitstable engines are due to go into a new museum in Whitstable. There is also the suggestion that the beam engine in the Science & Industry Museum in Manchester might be a Liverpool & Manchester engine due to it having reversing gear – very unusual in a standard industrial application. In the collection of the National Railway Museum at York are a pair of winding engines demonstrated by electric power daily, these being the Weatherhill engine – a vertical house-built engine – and the Swannington incline engine from Leicestershire. The latter is particularly significant due to its being an early horizontal engine and also one that uses a piston valve to distribute the steam as opposed to the slide valve used in most applications until the 1830s, when this engine was installed.

Did you know?

Recently, a splendid contemporary model of a side lever winding engine, built by Thomas Greener of Etherley, County Durham, has come to light. Greener was employed as an engine man on the Stockton & Darlington Railway and made the model in 1836, no doubt based on engines he knew in the locality. In 2018 it was displayed and demonstrated in steam on a number of occasions – possibly the oldest working model still to be steamed in the world.

This is probably the oldest steamable model steam engine in the world. Made in 1836 by Thomas Greener in County Durham, it is a well-observed engine showing many of the features seen on engines that the builder would have encountered in his working life.

3
Improving the Breed

Initially, the house-built beam engine was a very large affair, requiring a building to hold the engine up with a beam wall and strong foundations. This rather limited the size and applications of engines, but with the growth of higher-pressure engines, they no longer had to be built into a structure and could become free-standing. In the late eighteenth and early nineteenth centuries, the obstacles of patents still held sway, and a number of developments grew out of the desire to innovate and circumvent the restrictions. Engineers who were experimenting with the various facets of steam power tried their hand at motive power units, and the patent books are full of their exploits. One such was Matthew Murray of the Round Foundry in Leeds, who made commercially successful steam railway locomotives for that city in 1812. In an attempt to make a compact power source, he created the hypercycloidal engine – which had no crank and was thus only as wide as its flywheel and was self-supporting. Its rotative motion was ingenious and similar to Watt's sun and planet gear, only there was no connecting rod at all, just a piston rod with a gear on it rotating inside a gear tooth which drove the flywheel and drive shaft – much better to see in motion than describe here – and happily an example can be seen in steam at ThinkTank in Birmingham.

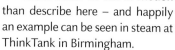

The space saving that self-contained engines allowed made the spread of steam power much, much faster as the engine could be built in a works as a stand alone unit and then be sent off to the final customer. Maudslay created the table engine, effective and compact, and later, in production, engineers such as Marshalls of Gainsborough mass produced inverted vertical engines which found use around the world, from tea plantations to steam breweries and many points in between.

Murray's hypercycloidal engine was an example of an attempt to make the steam engine more compact and space-efficient. Its unique action can still be seen as it is regularly run under steam at ThinkTank in Birmingham.

Above left: Another space-saving innovation was the Maudslay table engine, shown by this example in the Science Museum.

Above right: A typical inverted vertical or 'bottle' frame engine as made by Marshalls of Gainsborough in their thousands and used internationally. This one is being installed as a generating engine in a display at the Steam Museum at Straffan in County Kildare, Ireland.

Did you know?

The Istanbul Royal Mint in Turkey has a pair of Maudslay table engines in it, dating from 1841. The Mint only ceased production in 1967, but the engines remain, next to the Topkapi Palace.

Another reasonably common space-saving engine was the Grasshopper design, so-called due to the way it looked in operation, with a beam fixed at one end rather than in the centre. With a single bed, it was compact and easily installed. The traditional beam engine also remained in development and many later smaller engines had tank beds which made them into a single unit and also enabled their re-use and re-sale should a business fail or upgrade. A very fine compact vertical twin-cylindered pumping engine is preserved in situ

Drainage engines were many and varied in their type and style. On the Somerset Levels, the engine at Westonzoyland Pumping Station remains in situ and is steamed for visitors at the museum that has been established there.

at the Westonzoyland Pumping Station on the Somerset Levels, indicative of a once-numerous type doing a serious drainage job. This was paralleled in the East of England with drainage engines in the Fens, such as the preserved Dogdyke beam engine driving a drainage scoop wheel – like a waterwheel in reverse!

Colliery winding engines were a further breed apart – whether for hauling men or coal out of the mine, driving them was a skilled art as time and production, as well as men's safety, depended on the engineman. Beam engines, vertical engines and latterly compact or massive horizontal engines of two or more cylinders were used to wind efficiently and

Desford Colliery No. 2 shaft had this Wood & Gee winding engine, built as their number 1000. Installed in 1900, it worked until 1978. Mr Pallett, the engine driver, was at his seat when this picture was taken on 11 August 1968 – incidentally, the final day of steam on the British railway system!

quickly. Steam or electric braking systems were introduced, and devices were fitted to show the position of the cages down the shaft. The winding engine man was a revered figure in the pit, and his engine was quite often immaculate and very well maintained. As with steam all over the country, the use of the steam winder declined in the 1950s and 1960s as electricity took over or the pits closed. Nonetheless, the final steam winding engines were still in operation well into the 1990s, the very last being the Donisthorpe engine, which ceased in 1994 and is now preserved by Leicestershire Museums, albeit in a dismantled state.

The largest engines appeared in the early to mid-twentieth century. George Saxon made monstrous mill engines of several cylinders, and in Sheffield, the River Don and other rolling mill engines were of up to 12,000 horsepower for rolling armoured plate. They had air-operated valve gear to allow instant reversing as the hot plate could not be allowed to stand still during the rolling process. The River Don engine is a magnificent triple-expansion engine and is still demonstrated daily at the Kelham Island industrial museum. A few years ago, the author was talking to a lady who had worked at the steelworks and she told how each year, new female recruits to the works were taken into the engine room to see it operating at full tilt. While they were there, the engine would be reversed and if the recruits fainted, they would be placed in the offices while those still standing were deemed suitable to work on the shop floor. The River Don engine was one of four built in 1905, and it is now the most powerful steam engine still working in Europe.

An engine typical of a smaller winder can be visited at the National Coal Mining Museum for England at Caphouse Colliery. Made by Davy Bros, this one was in operation commercially on occasions up to 1981.

Above: The view from the driver's seat for Bagworth Colliery bottom seam. The control levers and depth dial can be seen in the foreground. Working until 1974, this engine was built by Worsley Mesnes.

Left: Nothing in any museum or heritage site can compare with the massive River Don engine at Kelham Island. Relocated and restored to steam in the 1980s, it is a sight to behold and a visit when it is working will never be forgotten!

Similarly, many large waterworks were equipped with triple-expansion engines of great horsepower capability in the first three decades of the twentieth century until electric pumps took over. These engines were often close relatives of the large triple-expansion engines finding favour in marine applications, driving thousands of ships around the world.

At the site of the former Astley Green colliery in Lancashire stands the largest surviving winding engine of its type in Europe. A twin tandem compound, built in 1912, it was rated at 3,300 horse power, winding both men and coal until 1970. Now preserved, since 2013 it has been able to be turned on compressed air. Elsewhere in the UK a number of smaller but still large winding engines have been preserved, significantly the ones at Chatterley Whitfield, Pleasley Colliery and Haigh Pit, though access is limited in the cases of the first and last of those. The National Coal Mining Museum for England has their much smaller winder in steam most days, kept much as it would have been when the colliery was still in operation.

Large engines could not start on their own and needed the pistons to be set at specific places in the cylinder to allow them to be set in motion. Thus, another application was

The large triple-expansion steam engine also found work in water and sewage applications. Fleming & Ferguson of Paisley made this engine and two sisters in 1900 for the London Road Sewage Pumping Station in Coventry.

Perhaps the finest late triple-expansion engines on display in the UK are those at Kempton Park waterworks. Working from 1927 until 1980, they were built by Worthington Simpson and each weighs 1,000 tons.

Yates & Thom of Blackburn made the immense colliery winding engine for Astley Green colliery in Lancashire in 1912. The pit closed in 1970 and volunteers have worked long and hard to be able to turn the engine over by compressed air.

Above: Haig Pit in Whitehaven was a museum until relatively recently, when financial troubles forced its closure. There are a pair of steam winding engines on site, this being the larger of the engines made by Bever Dorling and seen before restoration started.

Right: Typical of a barring engine, this is one fitted to the Kempton Park triple-expansion. The gear teeth in the larger engine's flywheel can be seen, and also the small holes in the flywheel of the barring engine, allowing it to be placed in the correct position for starting.

created, the barring engine – a small single or twin-cylindered steam engine to turn the flywheel over to the optimum position for the main engine to start. When engines were smaller, this could be done by hand with an iron bar located into holes in the rim of the flywheel, and the engine 'barred over', but as size increased, the practicality of doing it by hand ceased. The barring engine would engage gears on the flywheel until the right spot had been reached; then it would be taken out of gear, allowing the main engine to be started itself.

Did you know?

The author used to run a medium-sized beam engine at the now-closed Snibston Discovery Museum at Coalville in Leicestershire. The engine needed barring over by hand to clear the cylinder and get it in the right position to start, but at times would be so hard to bar over that the author could lift his feet off the floor and the flywheel still wouldn't turn!

Not every preserved location lasts forever. Snibston Discovery Museum in Coalville was closed in 2015 but housed a number of steam engines, including this Gimson beam engine – one of a pair that had been housed in a waterworks at Hopwas in Staffordshire. It was named *Woody* after one of the local doctors.

A very old vertical engine from the 1840s, displayed at the Anson Engine Museum near Poynton in Cheshire. Used in the stables at Adlington Hall, it shows the versatility of the steam engine and how it would appear in the most unlikely places.

The admission of steam into the cylinder and its efficiency was down to the valves used to allow steam in to do work and out to the condenser or exhaust. In reciprocating engines, many systems were devised from simple trip-operated valves with cams or levers to complex but very effective ways to manage steam. These were developed over time and different valve gears worked well in different applications. For a time, stationary and railway engines were similar, but as the drive for profits and fuel efficiency rose, the stationary engine moved ahead. Corliss valve gear was more effective in allowing the passage of steam with fewer large moving parts, being a semi-rotary gear, while later the Uniflow engine meant that steam passed through the cylinder in one direction only, meaning that steam did not go in and out of the same passages, as it did in conventional slide or piston valve engines.

Small engines had any number of uses, from within the engine house itself running an Economiser scraping flues or a steam pump supplying boiler water to an engine running a printing press or potato slicer. Small double diagonal engines were commonplace in Lancashire dye and bleach works while hardly being found anywhere else geographically in the country.

So far, this book has looked at the engines, but how was the power transmitted from the engine to the machinery it was driving? For pumps in mines and other applications such as water and sewage works, it was simple: a reciprocating pump was attached to one end of a beam engine or the piston rod of a horizontal engine. Rotative pumping engines saw the flywheel for stored energy evening out the operation and cycle of the engine, but the pump was still directly attached. For every other form of work, there was the need to transmit rotary power, whether it was for hauling, milling, or any number of other industrial processes. Initially, mills were gear-driven but this was costly and required much upkeep through oiling and maintenance. Belt and rope drives were much easier and cost-effective; latterly, line shafting allowed individual machines to be taken in and out of use by the operators using a clutch arrangement. Thousands of works across the country adopted this practice, and a number remain in situ either in heritage use or as vestigial parts of larger industrial concerns. A particularly fine installation is at the engineering works of the Isle of

On this horizontal engine shown at Bressingham Steam Museum in Norfolk, the pump is driven by the long rod from the flywheel and thence through ninety degrees via the bell crank in the foreground to the pump below.

Man Railway in Douglas. A number of industrial museums have similar setups, though the sad closure and later demolition of Snibston Discovery Museum in Coalville has denied us an accessible steam-driven workshop as all equipment is in store, including the very pretty little Gimson horizontal engine. The rope race to a mill is less well preserved, due in no small part to the loss of mills despite the engines being kept for posterity. The engine was the heart of every factory – if the engine failed, production stopped and money was lost. A large mill engine would be driving several thousand looms at once via the system of shafts, pulleys and belts, which could be engaged and disengaged at times of low production or for maintenance.

While there were many technical innovations and patents to improve the efficiency of the steam engine, some works were much simpler. In many textile mills, the engine flywheel would be boarded over to cut down the air resistance put up by the spokes as the engine turned over at speed. To stand in a mill engine house and hear nothing but the tick-ticking of the valve gear is one of the great steam experiences of the world and gives further credence to the description of the stationary engine as a gentle giant as the engine marks a steady 60–80 revolutions a minute. There were hundreds of these engines driving weaving sheds and spinning mills across the North of England and elsewhere, many working into the 1950s and 1960s.

John Chadwick of Manchester made this single-cylinder engine, located in the workshops of the Isle of Man Steam Railway at Douglas. While the workshops are now electrically driven, the steam engine can be piped up to one of the railway locomotives and run for special events.

A small steam-driven workshop was part of the display at the now-closed Snibston Discovery Museum at Coalville. The Gimson horizontal engine drove a belt to lineshafting which in turn ran a number of drills, shapers and planning machines – great fun to operate and demonstrate for the visitors.

So many mill engines were built and installed in the North West that finding a typical example to illustrate the type was a hard choice. Perhaps the best-known engine is the Trencherfield Mill engine in Wigan, dating from 1907 and made in Bolton by J. & E. Wood. It is rated at 2,500 horsepower.

Did you know?

The steam-powered textile mill was not just the preserve of Lancashire, Yorkshire or Cheshire. As far south as the woollen mills of Devon and Somerset, large steam mill engines and later turbines could be found at work. Coldharbour Mill at Uffculme in Devon still houses and runs its original Pollitt & Wigzell engine coupled to the rope race. The engine was made in Sowerby Bridge, Yorkshire!

As turbines and electric motors began to be developed in the place of reciprocating steam engines, the final flourishing included such things as enclosed cranks and forced lubrication, where the only moving part of the engine that could be seen was the flywheel. Most of these engines were compounds and used for electricity generation in varying sizes. Because of this application, the engines had to run as fast as reciprocating pistons would allow. Companies such as Bellis & Morcom, Allens of Bedford and Ashworth & Parker specialised in these engines and their simple, robust and easy to maintain nature meant that a number of these machines remained in use, either in mainstream power production or on stand-by, into the 1990s. At the end of their lives, not all were scrapped, and some engine dealers were still exporting enclosed generating sets at the end of the twentieth century. Innovations such

Above: Away from the industrial heartlands, the textile mills of Somerset and Devon held a number of steam engines as power sources, including Coldharbour Mill. The engine is regularly run under steam and has been joined by a number of other engines brought in from local industries.

Right: The high-speed enclosed generating sets by Bellis & Morcom of Birmingham were widespread in their market and greatly varied in size. An example which represents the thousands made was on display until 2015 at Snibston Discovery Museum. In its working life, it was installed at Princes Drive Sewage Pumping Station in Leamington Spa.

The drive for increased efficiency led to further developments in engine technology. The Willans central valve engine was another attempt to push steam engine performance to a higher level. This engine is in the collections of the Science Museum.

as those of Peter Willans continued to be made – in his engines, the steam valve went up the inside of the pistons and cylinders, making an effective and more efficient engine for electricity generation from 1884 onwards.

Did you know?

In a direct contrast to the long development of the steam engine over more than a century, its replacement in the form of the steam turbine went from prototype to production in less than ten years.

4

Personalities of Steam: The Builders and Operators

Building a steam engine began with the craft of the millwright, with engines constructed from timber and metal – the wooden beams being not so far removed from the technology that was known about and understood. Engineering grew out of this activity as materials changed and standards changed, with the limits and fits of parts becoming more crucial as the complexity of the engines increased. The need for skilled engineers to build these engines was realised by James Watt, who had improved the design of engines significantly. Although appearing crude by modern standards, James Watt's engines were some of the most advanced machines of their time, the Soho Foundry being the first factory in the world built specifically to allow construction of steam engines there from 1795. The new standards of precision had never been seen before and the workforce depended on more and more skilled engineers and artisans. The same precision, combined with the trade of engineer, set Britain apart as a world-leader at the time, giving rise to the reputation of the country as the 'Workshop for the World' during the nineteenth century.

By 1845, over 17,000 men worked in engineering around Manchester alone, and the export trade in engines was growing from an increasingly skilled workforce. Britain sold engines all around the world. Henry Maudslay in London was receiving orders for engines, as has been seen, from what is now Turkey, and also from Brazil as well as the home market. This was reflected in many places as the century progressed. Likewise, there were builders all over Britain – from Hayle to Glasgow/Leith and all places in between. In the North West, major builders like Galloways of Manchester were supported by Hick, Hargreaves of Bolton, Clayton, Goodfellow of Blackburn and dozens of others. Centres of engineering such as Leeds and Birmingham rubbed shoulders with other locations such as Lincoln, where a number of engine builders were congregated. Dorset had Hindleys of Bourton while in the Staffordshire town of Burton upon Trent, Thornewill & Warham along with Buxton & Thornley turned their hand to steam engines from brewery equipment. Some builders made thousands of engines and sold their products worldwide; some of the smaller makers built just one. General engineering companies built engines alongside their other production. Road vehicle manufactures Fodens of Sandbach built stationary steam engines, some of their rolling mill engines made for South Wales tinplate works remaining in the museum at Kidwelly to this date. On occasion, the works buildings for these companies still exist and are recognised, such as Matthew Murray's works in Leeds, while others have been demolished and have either been built upon or are now car parks. A further activity was simply that of dealing in engines but putting the dealer's name on the engine – a form of badge engineering, as it were – which has caused all manner of research challenges for the modern historian looking into the engine building practice. A rare insight into constructing a large stationary

Displays of engine builders and their history are few and far between in museums. Bradford Industrial Museum has this selection of makers' plates and photographs on show as part of their steam power gallery.

steam engine was published by the International Stationary Steam Engine Society, being the memoirs of a gentleman called Arnold Throp and entitled *The Last Years of Mill Engine Building*. It's well worth seeking out a copy.

The steam engine has always been seen as something of a character; it has been one of the few inventions created for human good and not to blow people up or drop bombs on them. It has been given human traits and often equated to the nearest thing that man has made to a living creature, for it needs feeding and responds to good or poor treatment. Little wonder then that some enginemen – for driving engines was solely a male preserve – developed a relationship with their charges. The blowing engines *David* and *Sampson* from Lilleshall ironworks and now at Blists Hill Museum, Ironbridge, were said to have had a driver who spoke to the engines when pressure was low. He would sit between the great steam cylinders with his head in his hands and coax each engine in turn. Likewise, more than one steam pumping station saw the driver set up a bed on the cylinder top level so that a driver could remain in the warm but also keep an eye on his charges through times of great water demand or troublesome mechanical or supply issues. It also says a great deal about the work ethic of the time!

Characters have abounded through the lives of these engines, from millwrights to engineers and all points in between, though as parallel with many of their more mobile cousins. The pioneers

While not the best quality image, this is the cylinder floor at Papplewick Pumping Station, where one of the enginemen set up his bed to keep an overnight watch on the engines!

like Richard Trevithick, known and revered across the world, were one thing; the everyday man or woman trying to make their way in the world are so often the unsung reality of the industrial steam engine. One sadly never hears the reminiscences of a mill engine driver, though a couple of publications in the last fifteen years have led to a greater understanding around the cognoscenti. The writings on the internet of Stanley Challenger Graham on the 'One Guy from Barlick' forum include the story of how he went from firebeater to engineer at Bancroft Mill in Barnoldswick in 1974. He worked there until its closure in 1978 and his description of running a commercial steam-operated mill is second to none. It is well worth reading to understand how a steam-powered business continued into the 1970s successfully but then declined and was closed. The decommissioning was a whole fascinating process in itself. The experience gained in this gave Stanley the great opportunity to work on the recommissioning of the Ellenroad Mill Engine in Rochdale in the 1980s; it now operates as a heritage attraction and is one of the largest surviving mill engines in the country. There is now but one complete steam weaving shed in the whole of the world: the mill at Queen Street, Harle Syke, in Burnley. It has been a heritage attraction since the early 1980s but has veered from viability to threatened artefact almost every decade since. It was closed in September 2016 but at the time of writing has re-opened on a limited basis, once again running under steam.

Driving a stationary steam engine is rather different to a railway locomotive or traction engine in that one does not have to respond to different routes or rail conditions and that once up and running under load, the governor takes care of regulating speed and power. One does have to make sure the engine crank is in the right position to start, but with some of the simpler single-cylinder horizontal engines, it really is a case of opening the stop valve and letting the engine come up to speed. The older beam engines and Cornish cycle engines are more of a challenge and I remember over twenty years ago watching the Crofton beam engines starting in an almost religious atmosphere with the driver as the great high priest, manipulating the valves by hand until the engine strokes were regular and he could put the valves onto the catch handles and let the engine run itself. Mishandling of a Cornish non-rotative pumping engine could result in a heavy overstroke with resultant danger of damage to the engine. The venerable Newcomen engine at Elsecar was run for the last time on steam for a filming crew in 1952. During the session, it came indoor too heavily on one stroke and cracked the cylinder, never to be run again. Likewise, with the rotative beam engines I have run, one has had to manage and adjust the vacuum in the condenser so it is in equilibrium and the engine can run steadily. A big issue for many preserved engines is the absence of a load to hold them back, and therefore the engine either needs a simulated load or to be operated or driven accordingly to prevent damage. Depending on where one is in the country, the engine has an engineman, a driver or a tenter/tender – and the person looking after steam production is either a fireman as on the railway, or the firebeater.

Boiler management is a separate craft, and boiler plant could be the subject of a book alone as steam producers developed. Starting with low-pressure haystack boilers, the technology moved to waggon top boilers and then for most industrial processes and applications,

Above left: The driving position of the Newcomen engine at Elsecar in South Yorkshire – very basic as, once the engine had been started, it could essentially drive itself.
Above right: At Crofton in Wiltshire, there are two Cornish cycle pumping engines sited for supplying water to the Kennet & Avon Canal. The driving position is more complex than that of the Newcomen engine, but the engine still ran automatically after being set in motion.

Right: The earliest steam producers were known as haystack boilers due to their shape. Low-pressure and fairly inefficient, they still provided steam for many engines for almost a century.

Below: Most engines from the nineteenth century onwards relied on single-flue Cornish and the twin-flue Lancashire boiler for their steam production. Operating either on their own or in banks of multiple numbers, this cut-away example at the Science and Industry Museum in Manchester allows the internal parts to be seen.

In boiler houses all over the country, boiler feed water was often provided by a steam pump on steady tick over. Many different sizes were made; this Weir pump is a medium-sized example.

the Cornish single flue or its development, the twin-flue Lancashire boiler, held sway for more than a century and a half. More complex Babcock water tube boilers saw use towards the end of commercial steam use, but only one installation survives to this day. If the steam plant was a smaller application, then another boiler type such as a Cochrane, Scotch or simple vertical boiler might suffice. These were faster to raise steam but could not produce steam in such sustained volumes. Collieries and pumping stations would have banks of boilers in a house together, and latterly the use of automatic stokers was introduced to save labour in keeping the grates covered. Water feed to the boilers was usually provided by either a reciprocating or rotative pump, which could be set away and run steadily to keep the water level up to cope with the demand for steam. The usual makers of these were Weirs, Evans or Worthington-Simpson, in all manner of sizes and arrangements – the study of these could make a book in itself!

Accidents were an everyday hazard of working with steam, with consequent damage to engines, men or both. Flywheels burst, connecting rods broke and the books of the old insurance companies were filled with incidents involving boilers and ancillary plant. With beam engines, the cast beam could break, and where this involved a mine pump or a man-engine transport system, the results were tragic. The result was the changing of materials and construction of beams – later beam engines having plate beams in several parts. A few of the older engines have strengthening braces or struts which can be seen, such as on the Kew engines, with the aim of preventing such incidents in case of breakage. Many stationary engines are heavily over-engineered to allow for the stresses they are subject to and also to mitigate against failure. The massive components of such engines as the Tower Bridge ones show the extent to which this was taken even as late as the 1940s.

5
Giving an Engine a Home: Houses and Heritage

Early engines are very much affairs of iron and timber, but their houses varied from place to place as to whether they were made from brick or local stone. The oldest surviving Newcomen engine, in its original house at Elsecar, is in a stone building, whereas the replica of the Newcomen engine at the Black Country Museum in Dudley is in a red brick structure, reflecting the production of those building materials in the locality. Near the site of the famous Bedlam Furnace in Ironbridge Gorge, industrial archaeologist Paul Vigor identified a Newcomen engine house for a furnace blowing engine in the late 1990s, repurposed as a domestic dwelling. Such survivors are indeed rare now. As the nineteenth century wore on and the use of iron grew more widespread, ornamentation began to creep in and engines, their houses and fittings started to mix form and function. The great engine houses at Kew are Georgian in style and would not look out of place in any townscape of that period. Architectural influences ran wild throughout the century, and a mix of classical, Gothic, Palladian and many others could be seen across the country. Often in an

industrial setting this went hand in hand with the architecture of the factory or mill itself, and some of the larger complexes were quite imaginative – Manningham Mills in Bradford, for example, being built in the Italianate style with a chimney very much like a campanile.

With the turn to the twentieth century, architectural styles changed further. The incredible brickwork and styling of the Bratch pumping station in Staffordshire is almost whimsical, with turrets and decorative changes of brick. By the 1920s, the massive installation at Kempton Park waterworks in West London reflected the Art Deco

The house of the Newcomen engine at Elsecar dates from the 1790s and is typical of the kind of structure that the eighteenth-century industrialists commissioned for their engines.

In the 1830s, the Metropolitan Water Board's new pumping station at Kew Bridge built this house to keep the first engines on site in. It would not be out of keeping in a street setting of the period and hardly looks industrial at all.

By the early twentieth century, the building of the water pumping station at The Bratch in Staffordshire reflected the tastes of the time and the use of brick and tiles in greater quantities. The stylistic features and embellishments were not necessary for a building housing essentially industrial plant, but make for a very attractive construction.

One of the last great engine houses is that of the Kempton Park engines from the late 1920s, in the Art Deco style. Its significance has been recognised by the building's listing as a Grade II* monument.

movement and its status as one of the last great buildings of the steam age is reflected in its listing as a Grade II* monument. That it survives intact with the engines it was built to house still inside is little short of marvellous. All over the country, many other engine houses still survive without their engines complete – York Waterworks' engine house, still visible from the East Coast Main Line railway just north of the city, is just one example. The splendid Gothic Whitacre pumping station in the Midlands remains in the middle of a still working installation, this also being the reason the building still stands!

Did you know?

Lendal Tower in York dates from around 1300 AD, but from the 1700s to 1836 it was home to a Newcomen engine. In 1674 Henry Whistler of London proposed a new scheme for supplying water and in April 1677 the tower was leased for 500 years to the York Waterworks Company. The tower was repaired, enlarged and heightened to take a lead cistern to which water could first be pumped into, prior to onward flow to the growing city. After Whistler's death a Col. William Thornton purchased the concern for £4,000, and then obtained a mortgage for £1,400 in order to install a Newcomen steam engine, of 4.7 horsepower. In 1781–4 John Smeaton (the father of civil engineering and designer of the famous Eddystone Lighthouses) rebuilt the engine to produce 18 horsepower to raise 10,500 gallons an hour. Drawings of the engine are displayed at the tower and evidence of its workings still exists at the mezzanine floor level on the heavy beams above. The improved engine worked in the tower until 1836, when it was moved to a new engine house.

If one were to convert a fourteenth-century tower to house industrial plant today, there would be uproar. However, Lendal Tower in York was rebuilt in the 1700s to house a Newcomen engine!

Inside the engine house or engine room, individual taste and expression held sway. Decorative ironwork came in, which had no purpose at all other than to look good! The ultimate expressions of this can be seen at Papplewick Pumping Station in Nottinghamshire and Crossness Engines in London. These were industrial installations which were not open to the public, but still looked fabulous and were kept in immaculate order by their enginemen. Floors were polished and tiled walls scrubbed; decorations were also often the order of the

Representing the finest engineering practice of the nineteenth century, when form and function went hand in hand, Dalton Pumping Station near Sunderland combines decorative style and grace with a pair of massive beam engines. If built today, it's unlikely that there would be as much expensive adornment, but we can be grateful that there was, as we can enjoy it today.

While many engines have been restored and repainted, a few engines remain in the paint schemes that they wore when in operation commercially. This small panel is an example of the detail and finish on the pumping engines at Ryhope in Sunderland, carefully conserved and protected.

day and examples of such can be seen in Holmes Mill in Clitheroe, where conservation has preserved and protected the wall coatings where so often restoration would have removed them. Truly, some engine houses were referred to as Cathedrals of Steam – but the human touch remained in the ornamentation and the care shown by the minders of the engines.

Did you know?

In textile mills, it is often said that the engine rooms were so clean that visitors were only allowed in if they removed their shoes!

The massive investment of ordering and buying a steam engine meant that the nineteenth century saw the growth of engineering merchants and dealers. If a works or mine closed, rather than scrap the large piece of equipment, the engine often found a new home at a new venue. It would be taken down piece by piece and re-erected, perhaps many miles away, to serve a new life of productivity at least one more time, if not to be moved again in its working career. Engine dealers grew up across the country. Some were established millwrights who turned their hand to steam and general engineering and others were new entrepreneurs. Into the early twenty-first century, the works of Thomas Mitchell & Son in Bolton bore witness to the company's history of buying, selling and repairing steam engines. Their assiduous record keeping showed how many engines had passed through their hands, while a visit into the warehouse was a voyage into the heritage of the company. Even though the company specialised latterly in pumps, a walk through the stores revealed any number of boiler feed pumps, a couple of Robey horizontal engines, several Ashworth & Parker or Browett & Lindley steam generating sets and even the beam from a long-dismantled engine – all listed on the computer stock database! Sadly, the company went into voluntary liquidation in 2007, leaving a legacy in the steam history of the North of England. Their story was but one of dozens like it.

The preservation of steam engines fits well within the post-industrial study and rescue of historic artefacts, which accelerated after the Second World War, and the writings of such people as the engineering historian Tom Rolt and Michael Rix, who coined the phrase 'industrial archaeology'. Windmills and similar buildings had been saved throughout the twentieth century by individuals and groups such as the Society for the Preservation of Ancient Buildings, so why not old steam engines? The steam locomotive and the steam traction engine had begun to be kept, so why not the stationary steam engine? In truth, engines had been

The National Museum of Scotland was established in the 1860s and began collecting old engines when they became available. This Watt rotative engine dates from 1786; it drove a brewery in Southwark and at the end of its ninety-nine-year career entered the museum in Edinburgh, where it can still be seen.

It's hard to get a photograph showing the Newcomen engine at Dartmouth in its entirety, but this image gives an impression of how basic an early engine really was. Well worth seeking out if in the area, it is a fitting tribute to Newcomen to see the engine in his home town.

saved for posterity for much longer than the 1950s – the collections of some of our great museums contain some really important engines; the pivotal points of steam power development are illustrated in the collections of the Science Museum in London. There, engines such as *Old Bess* and the famous 'Lap Engine' were placed in the 1860s and in following years. Today, a visit to the collection in South Kensington is a must for any student of steam engineering, and the mill engine which forms the centrepiece to the display is still operated on occasion under steam –

surrounded by its illustrious predecessors, one of which is a Newcomen engine which worked from 1791 to 1918, an amazing feat! Henry Ford collected engines like the old *Fairbottom Bobs* and took them over to his museum in Detroit.

In 1963, the Newcomen Society acquired a 1725 Newcomen engine which had survived latterly at Hawkesbury Junction on the Coventry Canal as a pumping engine and took it to Newcomen's birthplace of Dartmouth. There it was re-erected in a purpose-built building as the Newcomen Memorial Engine and it remains on public display, being gently moved by hydraulic power for visitors to see. A fully working replica Newcomen engine was built and commissioned by the Black Country Museum at Dudley in the 1980s and allows the cycle of operation to be seen in the area where the first Newcomen engine was located back in 1712. The oldest engine preserved in its original location is the delightful 1795 Newcomen engine preserved at Elsecar, near Barnsley. Last worked by steam in the 1950s, it was restored for hydraulic operation and demonstration in 2014. It is open for viewing through the engine house door daily, and tours are regularly offered to allow closer access.

A further very old engine is the Ocker Hill engine now at ThinkTank museum in Birmingham and formerly with the old Birmingham Museum of Science & Industry where it was put back

ThinkTank in Birmingham is the home to a number of interesting steam engines, most of which can be demonstrated under power. The Ocker Hill beam engine dates from 1779 and is now the oldest working steam engine in the world.

into steam in 1983, having initially been set aside by Birmingham Canal Navigations in the 1890s – a remarkably forward-thinking exercise. Having been built in 1779, it is now the oldest working steam engine in the world and is demonstrated regularly. The author saw it after its first restoration in the 1980s and found it a most unusual experience compared to the later engines he was used to – this one creaked and thumped!

On the Kennett & Avon Canal, the Cornish engines at Crofton in Wiltshire remain operable and are the oldest working engines of their type in their original location doing the job they were built for. In the care of a Trust since 1968, they are regularly steamed for visitors. In 2009 the modern pumps failed, and the steam engines once again worked for their living while repairs were undertaken.

Municipal museums were pioneers of preserving engines when the concept of private preservation had yet to take off. Birmingham, Manchester, Bolton, Bradford, Leeds, Halifax: all have collections of steam engines and a number run theirs under power, dating from the 1970s and early 1980s when industrial museums and collections were very much in vogue. They are still worth a visit today, showing the enduring appeal of steam power in operation to the visitor. With engines being made in many towns across Britain, a good number of smaller museums also hold engines in their collections, either models or full-size. For example, Chesterfield Museum has a small example of a Markham engine made in the town, while the classical Bowes Museum has a number of small model engines; one built by R. Cairns of Darlington in 1872 was exhibited at the Shildon Horticultural and Industrial Show of 1879, where it won first prize.

The late twentieth century saw a number of private museums grow and flourish – from those created by a society such as the Northern Mill Engine Society, whose struggle to

Above: Bradford Industrial Museum is one of the major regional public museums which demonstrates their collection in steam regularly.

Right: Many local museums have examples of full-size or model engines on display. Chesterfield Museum shows this small vertical engine made by the manufacturer Markham, based in the town.

establish a museum in Bolton saw them move premises completely in the 1990s, to the visions of men such as Dr Rowan Frances at Forncett St Mary in Norfolk, or Tom Nuttall whose Markham Grange Museum in South Yorkshire is but a stone's throw from the modern A1 road. All are worth supporting and even in 2018–19 new projects arise – the previously internal combustion engine museums of Internal Fire in West Wales and the Anson Museum in Poynton, Cheshire, both have significant steam sections now and run their engines under power to great acclaim. In 2018 Internal Fire took the large Willans central valve engine from the former GEC works in Rugby and, after decades of inactivity, have restored it to steam in a matter of months.

While there are a number of engines preserved in situ, or out of their original houses, perhaps one of the most unusual but, in the author's view, greatest heritage successes of recent times was the challenge of Holmes Mill in Clitheroe, Lancashire. Home to a superb tandem cross-compound engine by Clayton, Goodfellow of Blackburn, the engine had lain untouched for decades since the mill ended with steam. In the decades since, there had been many preservation schemes in Lancashire; some have been completed and the engines opened to the public while others, such as Grane Mill, continue to be worked on, and of course the saddest of all are the engines that have been lost, such as the Dee Mill disaster. Holmes Mill was known about, but the engine remained inaccessible and locked away until development of the mill became a real possibility in the twenty-first century. Innovative thinking has seen the mill become a hotel, food outlet and pub all in one, with the engine

One of the major independent collections of steam engines is Markham Grange in South Yorkshire. Attached to a plant nursery, the engines are run using steam from the garden enterprise's boiler. A wide variety of machines can be seen, perhaps the star being *Agnes*, a Pollitt & Wigzell mill engine made for a mill in Holmfirth, West Yorkshire.

Above: In recent years, the Anson Engine Museum near Poynton in Cheshire has created a steam hall. As a widely respected borrower from other museums, they have been able to install engines from Beamish Museum's collection as well as this rather lovely small beam engine on loan from Birmingham Museum & Art Galleries. It was made in 1872 by John Fowler of Leeds, better known for locomotives and road engines.

Right: This large Willans & Robinson central valve generating engine was displayed for many years at the Alstom works in Rugby, in the private museum set up there. Recent works changes saw the engine moved in 2018 to Internal Fire in Cardigan, West Wales, and it was very shortly back in steam.

taking centre stage in the Beer Hall. What's lovely is that as the mill is Grade II listed, the engine and house have been carefully and sympathetically cleaned and conserved, so that original features and paintwork remain. All around the engine room, the wall decoration and flooring are still as it was, with the gas pipes and light fittings intact and the very bare minimum of clear barriering around the engine to protect it, and also protect the customers from various oily parts. A few incongruous pot plants bring colour, but otherwise the engine is untouched, and still coupled to the rope race, which is a nice feature. Also, in appropriate framing on the engine room walls are plans of the engine and correspondence between the mill engineers and suppliers. It goes without saying that the food and beer are excellent, and should one be on a pilgrimage around steam engine sites in the North West, this is one that should not be missed.

Still, engines are lost even now. Around 2010, colleagues at work alerted the author to a 'steam engine in a skip' in a North East scrapyard where they had been looking at diesel shunting locomotives. Curiosity piqued, I made an appointment to go and see, and discovered a George Waller of Stroud horizontal engine, gas exhauster and a Sissons enclosed engine all in a skip, but intact – even down to the glass in the mechanical lubricator. They had been removed from a local gas works in 1967, and had remained in the scrap yard for decades, as the scrap man had a soft spot for old machinery and had thoughts about restoration at

Holmes Mill in Clitheroe is a superb redevelopment of a former textile installation with the engine preserved in its entirety, conserved and unrestored with all original fittings in the engine room. The rope race drive to the mill has also been kept and tables and guards around the engine are very understated, to allow the machinery to stand for itself.

The one that got away! A George Waller of Stroud engine in a skip in a North East scrapyard in March 2010. Despite having survived over thirty years in the yard, it was lost a couple of years later.

some point. I made an offer, which was considered but eventually turned down as the idea of restoration was suggested again by the yard owner. A couple of years later, a friend was looking for a small horizontal engine; I pointed him in the direction of the yard and off he set with some cash. Unfortunately, unknown to the yard owner, a staff member had dropped the engine to remove the bearing brasses, and the engine became worthless – thus the Waller and Sissons became examples of the ones that got away. Proof that it's always worth checking in skips and scrap yards!

Steam power in commercial use finished on the railways between the 1960s and 1980s. It finished on road construction in the 1980s, but stationary steam continued into the twenty-first century – just! There have been occasions where preserved pumping engines have replaced electric pumps that have failed on canals in recent years, or electricity generating sets kept on stand-by, but for day in, day out use, the final steam engine at work on a weekly basis was much smaller. In the Oxfordshire village of Hook Norton, the brewery that bears the same name ran a small Buxton & Thornley engine which drove the entire complex. In 1990, the author had a morning off school to go and visit the brewery in operation and, as a teenager born after the end of commercial road and rail steam, was delighted to see the engine working hard, belted up to the machinery. Still in situ in 2018, it now has preserved status rather than being the workhorse of industry that it was. Several other engines remain unpreserved and in situ, the two best known being the survivors at Glyn Pits near Pontypool.

At Hook Norton Brewery in Oxfordshire, the single-cylinder Buxton & Thornley engine was installed in 1899 and worked for over a century, becoming the last commercially used steam engine in the UK. It is still able to power the brewery but is now only used during brewery tours and on other special occasions.

Real dinosaurs of industry, they are still in their original houses, which were ruinous but have at least had temporary roof covers placed over them. The same status stands for the previously mentioned Dorothea beam engine in North Wales. There are still mill engines in Somerset and the North West that have not been seen for decades and slumber on – whether their fate is preservation or destruction, who knows? In Derbyshire, two engines remain in a clayworks, known about and safe – for now. Perhaps the imaginative redevelopment of Holmes Mill in Clitheroe will be the inspiration for more similar schemes.

6
What Next?

Unlike railway enthusiasm, there are not huge numbers of national societies catering for the stationary steam engine. What exists are bodies like the Newcomen Society for the Study of Engineering and Technology, the International Stationary Steam Engine Society (ISSES), and the Trevithick Society, which covers the man himself but also the steam engine in Cornwall. In that county, several engines are in the care of the National Trust and accessible to the public. These were preserved in the 1930s, long before it was fashionable or widespread to keep engineering for posterity. The ISSES publish regular newsletters, an annual journal and also a directory of engines open to the public – and dates for those shown to visitors under steam.

The preservation of engines has already been touched upon in the previous chapter, and this can vary from a single enthusiast with an engine or two to local groups such as that at Grane Mill, Haslingden, restoring a Stott mill engine, or the groups in South Staffordshire fighting to keep a few waterworks engines secure and give them a future. One can be a volunteer at an established museum such as the Anson or be a pioneer with some of the unrestored engines still out there, like Glyn Pits at Pontypool – almost engines in the wild. The challenge of the very

At Haslingden in Lancashire, David Arnfield and friends have been steadily restoring the S. S. Stott compound engine at Grane Mill. David is a pioneer of stationary steam preservation and his dedication is reflected in dozens of locations around the country, and new help is always welcomed.

Preservation of a full-size engine is beyond the means and ability of many. However items from engines appear for sale occasionally and collecting such items can be rewarding. This Thornewill & Warham builder's plate came off a Nottinghamshire colliery winding engine but was found in a junk shop in West Wales.

lovely but isolated Dorothea beam engine in Snowdonia remains. Occasionally engine makers' plates or other relics turn up in antique shops or in auction houses, and it can be a pleasant thing to seek out a few engine relics to keep on display around the house.

Since the Aeolipile of Hero, small-scale engines have been made, either for experimental purposes, sales of products or pleasure – the pleasure of owning, making or simply operating or playing with a steam engine. Model engines were made by watchmakers and instrument makers and it was with one of these that James Watt learned his craft by improving and fitting with a separate condenser to a Newcomen engine. Throughout the nineteenth century, models continued to be built, increasingly by amateurs as the years went by, though instrument makers such as Chadburns and Negretti & Zambra were notable makers. We have already seen how in 1836, the sixteen-year-old Thomas Greener of Etherley in County Durham built a small version of the side lever winding engine similar to that which he was familiar with from the local inclines on the Stockton & Darlington Railway. In 2018, that model was returned to working order and demonstrated under steam by its owner at presentations in the UK. It is now perhaps the oldest working steam engine model in the world, though it is now fired by gas rather than hot iron bars as it would have been when new. From the amateur engineers, the craft of model engineering grew; models were made either entirely from scratch or eventually from commercial drawings and castings made available from firms such as Stevens Model Dockyard or Bassett-Lowke. Models were entered in shows of work and competitions, and societies grew up to cater for the model engineer, though it must be said that this now encompasses railway locomotives, clocks, traction engines and internal combustion engines too, and in the twenty-first century not so many stationary steam engines are being made. There is a lively trade in these engines though for collectors and enthusiasts, and the internet auction houses and websites have enhanced this. Many model engines can be found in museums and collections across the country and are always worth looking out for. Many now destroyed engines or unusual designs now exist only in model form – and of course they take up much less space than the full-size equivalent.

Steam toys grew out of the desire to play with technology and move away from model engineering to affordable engines and is a subject for a book in itself, but from mass produced German steam engines before the First World War, the English trade took off in the 1920s, flourished briefly, and is now occupied solely by the long-established Birmingham company of Mamod (short for Malins Models), who must have made millions of toy steam engines in their eight decades of existence. The lure of live steam remains strong. These vary from simple single-cylinder engines to complex twin-cylinder reversible engines, while a variety of machine tools and accessories can be purchased for the engines to drive. For the collector, second

Above left: Model engineering is another way into enjoying stationary engines in a small space – either through building an engine or acquiring a ready-made example. The hobby has been around for well over a century and a half; this example was made in the late nineteenth century and is typical of many surviving in public and private collections all over the country.

Above right: Toyshop steam. The engines made by Mamod of Birmingham have been enjoyed by generations since the 1930s and the company still makes engines today. Collectors also look out for earlier engines: as a boy, the author longed for the ultimate twin-cylinder model. Forty years later, he got one!

hand engines provide a happy hunting ground while some specialist makers such as Maxwell Hemmens still provide limited runs of stationary engine models. It's possible to have live steam in the home for quite a lot less than £100; what other hobby offers such a cheap entry level?

Steam and vintage rallies across the country can sometimes turn up a stationary steam engine or two. Some owners of steam traction engines have small engines piped up to their larger charges and operate them on display next to their mobile cousins. A number of the semi-portable over and undertypes can be seen from time to time, with a pair mounted permanently at the Weeting rally site in Suffolk. A few people have placed a stationary engine and boiler in a lorry body and take them around the rallies, demonstrating the versatility of these engines although they were not built to be taken from place to place – thus the stationary engine reaches a wider audience than otherwise might be the case.

Away from physically helping at a preservation site or joining the ISSES, it's quite possible to enjoy stationary steam engines on a purely personal level of course, visiting museums and engines in museums. It's also quite fun to find engines in other unexpected places. In Lancashire in particular there are a number of engines preserved municipally – there's a small engine in Bury town centre, in Bolton is a Hick Hargreaves engine in a glass house in the town centre and to the north, in Darwen, a pair of engines are preserved in the open, one a cross-compound mill engine outside India Mill and up by the M66 a much smaller,

It's unusual to think of moving stationary steam engines around, but a number were made to be 'portable' between sites when the need for power changed. This Garrett of Leiston overtype semi-portable engine has returned home to the place of its manufacture for display in the Long Shop Museum, Leiston.

Above: The traditional steam rally of traction engines and such like can also be a happy hunting ground for engines. Geoff Baker of the Anson Engine Museum has some stationary engines mounted in the back of a lorry which he takes to shows, bringing a new audience in touch with our heritage.

Right: Several engines are on open display in various places around the country. In Darwen, Lancashire, there are two. The first is this vertical wall-mounted engine from the 1850s, typical of the smaller engine where it was built into the structure of the mill.

Outside India Mill in Bolton is this J. & E. Wood of Bolton engine, which drove one of the mill's weaving sheds from 1905 to the 1970s. Well cared for and regularly painted, it provides a visual reminder of the past to all who pass by.

A more unusual place to see a beam engine is Loughborough University. James Watt & Company made it in 1850 and it pumped at a London waterworks until 1933. The Metropolitan Water Board presented it to the university in 1934, since when it has been displayed with its Cornish boiler alongside.

older wall-mounted vertical engine; all of these are a delight to find, and do of course stand as testament to our industrial past for the passer by, not just the enthusiasts.

The Association for Industrial Archaeology caters for the interested enthusiast, not just for the engines themselves. Recording industrial complexes and processes as well as the machinery, they produce a regular Bulletin and a more in-depth Journal. It's well worth joining as often some serious engine research and archaeology takes place and is written up. It's fascinating to find out more about engines and locations that may have gone, and that's a study in itself – many engine houses and mountings remain, long after the engines themselves have gone, such as Swannington incline and Snarestone Pumping Station in Leicestershire. Interpreting what was there is great fun and of course informs future historians.

It might be considered that stationary steam engines have a limited appeal and thus are a more esoteric part of steam heritage. However, they figure greatly in high street publications such as the monthly magazines *Old Glory* and *Vintage Spirit,* where regular articles feature restoration or preservation schemes as well as individual engine or history sites. One can collect engravings and prints of engines, or catalogues of some of the longer-lived manufacturers. Many books have been published about the steam engine. The earliest antiquarian books by people such as Dr Dionysus Lardner are highly collectable, but many nineteenth-century primers on the steam engine can be bought much more affordably. *The Steam Engine* by David Kinnear Clark in its four bound volumes is a super text on the engine from a contemporary viewpoint, while in the early twentieth century, a similar series, *Modern Power Generators*, covers steam but also its competitors and equivalents. The illustrations in these books are also noteworthy.

As the end of steam in commercial use began to become evident, as with railways and agricultural steam, several enthusiast books appeared. The most notable were the writings and photographs of the late George Watkins, who made it his life's work to photograph as many stationary steam engines as possible before they were destroyed. Initially, he published a number of books on the textile mill engine and the general stationary engine in the 1960s and 1970s, but in the twenty-first century, many of his photographs were published in a major series of books looking at the engines in a regional context and then by makers. A tour de force, it is a definitive record of the final years of steam in industry, most of which is no longer in existence. Watkins' papers and photographs are now held as a research resource with Historic England in Swindon. Many other books have been produced, either about

Ephemera, books and paperwork are all collectable as well. The development of Holmes Mill at Clitheroe has allowed some of the correspondence relating to the engine there to be framed and put on display.

specific manufacturers or sites, and the photo album so often seen in other subjects is scarce. Guide books to museums are often excellent publications as well, the recent one for the London Museum of Water & Steam being a small book in its own right.

A more physical presence has been the use of some of the engines and their houses as community centres, not just preserving heritage but providing hubs for people to meet. Perhaps the most successful of these is the winding engine at New Tredegar in South Wales, where the engine is preserved in its original house and demonstrated regularly. Alongside this is a new building which provides meeting rooms and a café to the local community who have taken the engine to become a centre for their social activities rather than simply the preserve of steam enthusiasts – worthwhile as that activity is!

On the internet, the growth of social media has meant that pictures and information can be shared much more readily than they could be in the days of solely printed information. People have scanned their photos and made them accessible and share them, a pioneer of this being Richard Adamek with his Old Engine pages on the web; sadly these are no longer available. Since then, preservation sites and enthusiasts have set up websites, and the photo-sharing sites allow far more pictures than even the most comprehensive gazetteer. The Geograph.org.uk website is a fantastic resource, with many photos of engines from ISSES members giving national coverage. On Facebook, the author set up a Stationary Steam Engine page, and there are many others, often with an international or model-based angle as well. Whatever your interest in steam, the stationary engine world has something for you!

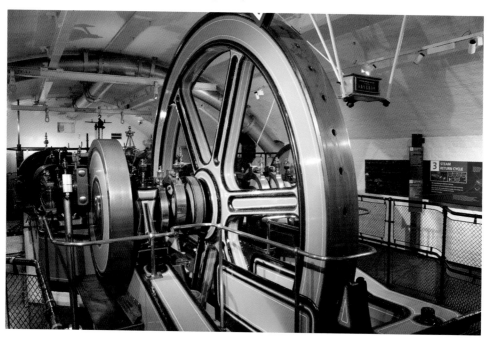

Of all locations to have a steam engine still in situ, perhaps London's Tower Bridge is the most iconic in the eyes of the general public. A pair of Armstrong pumping engines are in place and form part of the visitor experience. They were used to provide hydraulic power to raise and lower the bridge and one turns under compressed air for display.